COLOURS
YELLOW

First published in Great Britain in 2016 by Wayland

ISBN: 978 1 5263 0197 0
10 9 8 7 6 5 4 3 2 1

Wayland
An imprint of
Hachette Children's Group
Part of Hodder & Stoughton
Carmelite House
50 Victoria Embankment
London EC4Y 0DZ

An Hachette UK Company
www.hachette.co.uk
www.hachettechildrens.co.uk
A catalogue for this title is available from the British Library

Printed and bound in China

Produced for Wayland by
White-Thomson Publishing Ltd
www.wtpub.co.uk

Editor: Izzi Howell
Designer: Rocket Design (East Anglia) Ltd
Picture researcher: Steve White-Thomson
Wayland editor: Vicky Brooker

The author Gabrielle Woolfitt is a qualified teacher, specialising in science.

Picture acknowledgements:
The author and publisher would like to thank the following agencies and people for allowing these pictures to be reproduced:

iStock: Christopher Futcher 5c, dirk ercken 10b, ssucsy 18c; Shutterstock: Fotoluminate LLC cover, Kardash title page, Hanoi Photography 4t, Valery Bareta 4b, maradon 333 5t, RazvanZinica 5b, ifong 6, Abramova Elena 7t, Kenishirotie 7l, Andrey_Kuzmin 7r, travellight 7b, Natursports 8l, Nagel Photography 8r, Gelpi JM 9t, FiledIMAGE 9c, Nadezhda Zaruchevskaia 9b, Grezova Olga 10t, anat chant 10c, Ireneusz Waledzik 11, Romas_Photo 12t, oliverrees 12b, Tischenko Irina 13, Monkey Focus 14, Sailorr 15t, Artens 15bl, Martin Fowler 15br, Roger de Montfort 16l, Vixit 16r, Lenar Musin 17t, Eric Patterson 17bl, SABPICS 17br, corlaffra 18t, Scanrail1 18cl, Skylines 18cr, Jaroslav Moravcik 19, jiangdi 20t, Umpaporn 20cl, takepicsforfun 20cr, Mariyana M 21, Triff 22, izuboky 23t, Gladskikh Tatiana 23b, Nerthuz 24t, Stuart Monk 24b, FiledIMAGE 25t, michaeljung 25b, mihalec 26, Sergey Novikov 27, FamVeld 28t, Anneka 28b, bigacis 30, Photosiber 31.

All design elements from Shutterstock.

CONTENTS

WHAT IS YELLOW?

Yellow is a **BRIGHT** colour. Yellow clothes can make people **CHEERFUL**.

Yellow is a **SUNNY** colour.

RIPE CORN is yellow. Have you ever walked through a **CORNFIELD**?

A sandy beach is **YELLOW**.

Do you know how to build a **SANDCASTLE**?

Write a **STORY** or a **POEM** about a yellow day. Where do you go? What yellow plants and animals do you see?

YELLOW FOOD

Which yellow fruits taste **SWEET** and which taste **SOUR**?

How many kinds of **YELLOW FRUITS AND VEGETABLES** can you name in this photo?

SOYA BEANS are good for you.

What yellow food do you spread on **BREAD**?

Some cooking oil is made from **SUNFLOWERS**.

Yellow split peas can be made into **DHAL**.

Make a list of yellow **FOODS**!

YELLOW ANIMALS

Yellow labradors make **GREAT PETS!**

These **YELLOW FISH** stand out against the coral reef.

All baby birds grow inside **EGGS.**

Here is a baby chick. The chick's **YELLOW FEATHERS** keep it warm.

They use the yellow egg yolk as **FOOD.**

This chick will change as it gets older. It will lose its yellow feathers and grow into a chicken.

Quack!

What will these baby birds grow into?

POISON YELLOW

Some yellow animals use poison.

Wasps and bees can **STING** you. Their sting has **POISON** in it.

You can neutralise the poison. Use **BAKING-SODA** for a bee sting. Use **VINEGAR** for a wasp sting.

Some people living in rainforests in Brazil use poison darts for hunting. The poison comes from yellow frogs. They are called **POISON DART FROGS**.

A wasp
close
up looks
SCARY!

YELLOW SHAPES

This shape is called a **SPHERE**.

A sphere is a **SOLID SHAPE**.

Grapefruit are **ALMOST SPHERES**.

This shape is called a **CUBE**.

What shape is this famous building in **EGYPT**?

A hexagon is a flat shape with six sides.

Hexagons **FIT TOGETHER** without any gaps.

Which other shapes **FIT TOGETHER** without gaps?

Do **SPHERES** fit together well?

Bees keep their **HONEY** in cells shaped like hexagons. They make the cells out of **WAX**.

YELLOW FLOWERS

This huge yellow sunflower grew from a **SMALL SEED.**

Insects like yellow flowers. They collect pollen from one flower and carry it to another.

Some yellow flowers grow in gardens and parks. Others grow in woods, like this **PRIMROSE**.

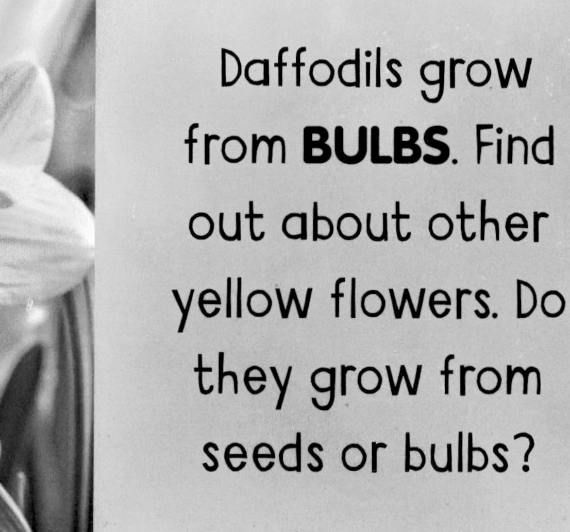

Daffodils grow from **BULBS**. Find out about other yellow flowers. Do they grow from seeds or bulbs?

YELLOW DESERTS

The sun cracks rocks to make sand. Wind blows the sand around.

SNAKES live in deserts. Some hide in the sand to keep cool.

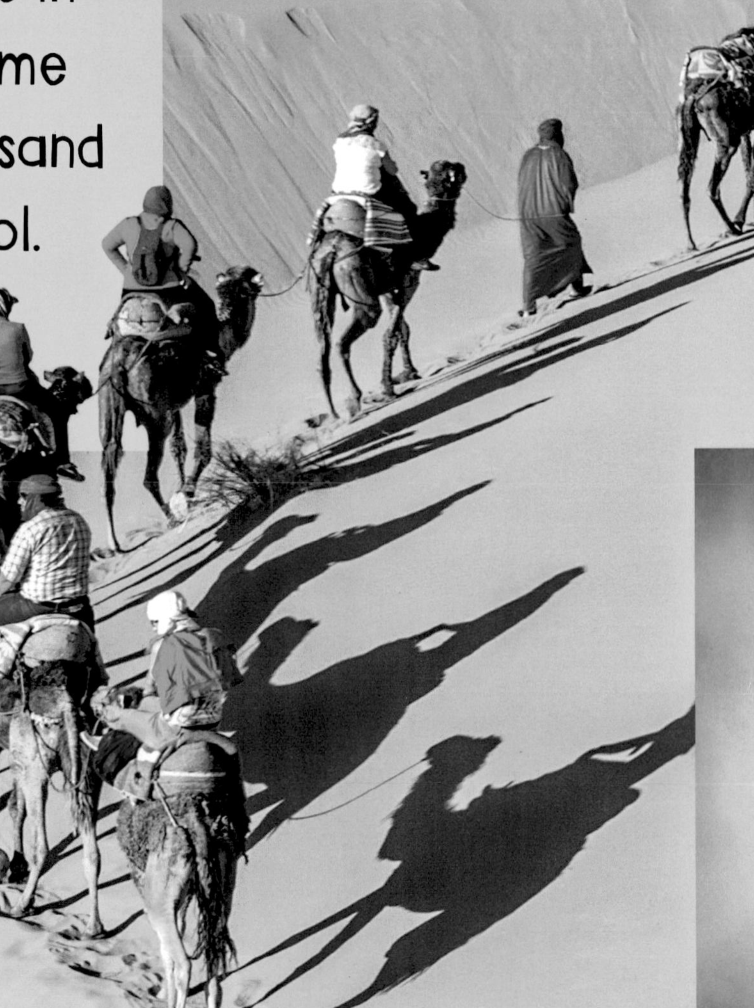

Only a few plants, such as prickly cacti, can grow in deserts.

Yellow deserts are dry. There is very little rain.

A camel can live in the desert. It carries fat in its hump. It uses the fat as food.

A camel has **BIG, FLAT FEET** for walking on sand.

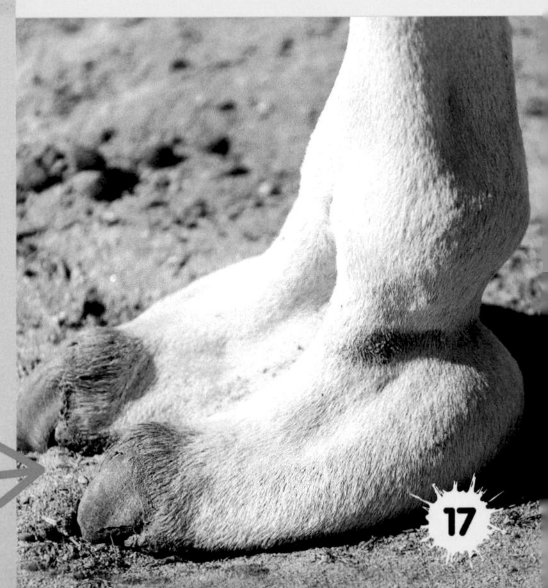

GOLD

This is a **GOLD NUGGET**. It car be melted and made into ...

gold bars ...

gold coins ...

and a gold ring.

Gold does not **RUST**.

Gold is a very **SPECIAL METAL**.

Thin strips of gold are easy to bend.

This gold mask is more than **THREE THOUSAND** years old.

It looks as **SHINY** today as it did when it was made.

SPICY YELLOW

Spices are parts of plants.

Ginger is a knobbly kind of **ROOT**.

It has a hot and spicy taste.

This is **TURMERIC** powder.

Spices add **COLOUR** and **TASTE** to food.

Here is a spicy

THAI CURRY.

Saffron is a very expensive spice. It is made from parts of **CROCUS FLOWERS**.

Mustard is a **SEED**. It is ground into **POWDER**.

Do you like **MUSTARD** on your sausage?

Don't put too much on...

It's hot!

YELLOW SUN

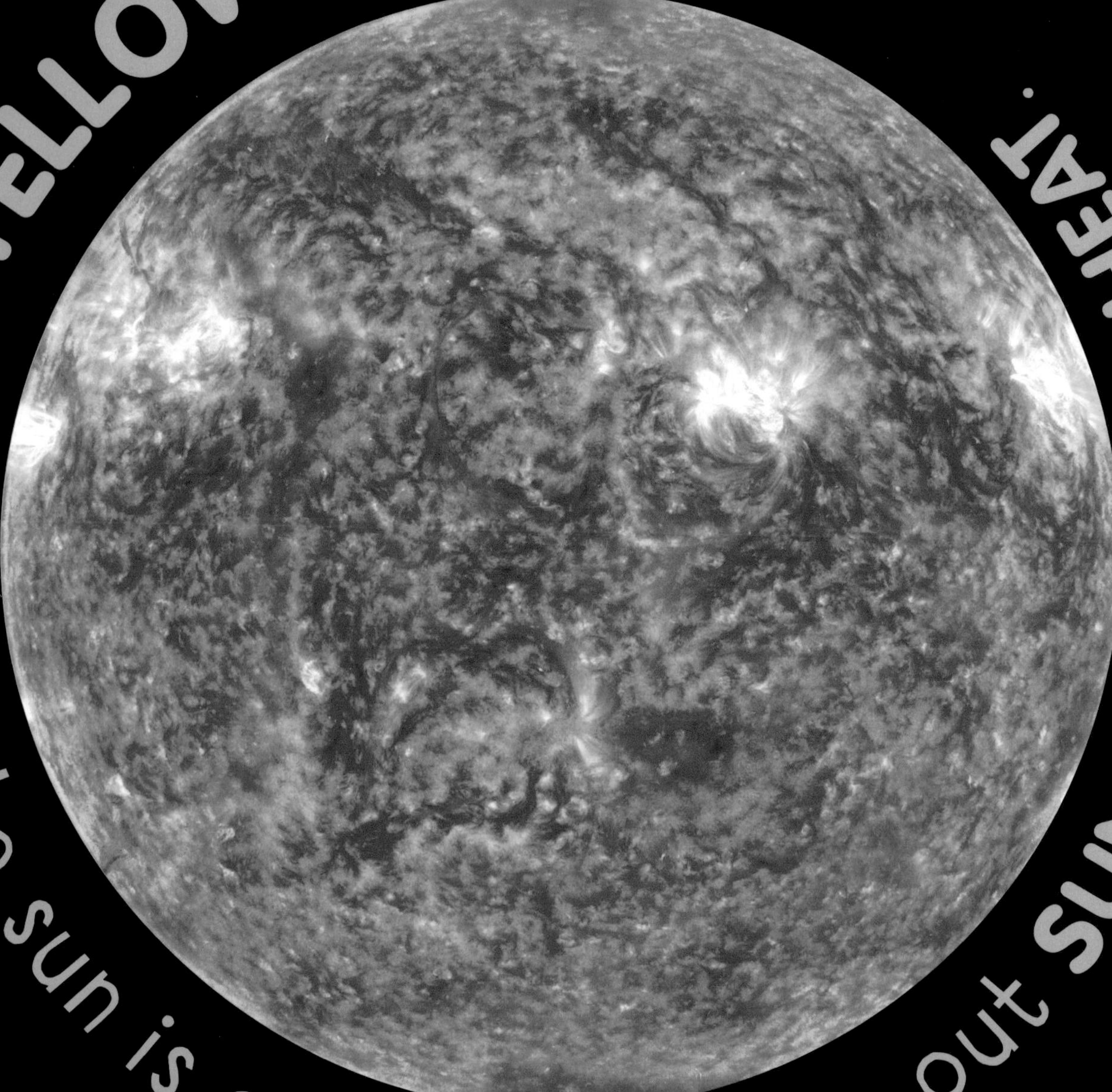

The sun is a **STAR**. It gives out **SUNLIGHT** and **HEAT**.

How is a **SHADOW** made? You can see your shadow on a **SUNNY DAY**.

When something is left in bright sunlight it **HEATS UP**.

What has happened to this girl's **ICE CREAM**?

BRIGHT YELLOW

Yellow is a bright colour. It shows up well.

Yellow cars have **FEWER ACCIDENTS**. Other car drivers can see them coming.

American **SCHOOL BUSES** are yellow, too.

Yellow can warn us about **DANGERS**. What are these signs warning us about?

Some workers wear yellow because it makes them **EASIER TO SEE**.

YELLOW IN AUTUMN

In the autumn, corn and other crops turn yellow. They are ready for harvesting.

Try mixing different colours to paint an **AUTUMN PICTURE**.

Add a tiny bit of **RED**. What colour do you get?

Slowly add **MORE RED** – watch the colour change!

In the autumn, many leaves change colour. They turn from green, to yellow, to red.

YELLOW PARTY

Yellow is used in festivals.

Christian people celebrate **EASTER**. Look at these Easter bunnies!

Some people paint **EGGS** at Easter.

Yellow chicks decorate this **EASTER HAT**.

Here is a yellow **BIRTHDAY** party.
Can you see ...

... **BALLOONS**?
Can you
count them?

... a yellow **PRESENT**
wrapped up in a
yellow ribbon?

yellow straw

... a birthday
CUPCAKE with
some candles
on it? **HOW
MANY?**

yellow
cups

MAKE IT YOURSELF

Please ask an adult to help you with this project.

MAKING BUTTER

You will need:

- ★ a big jar with a tight-fitting lid
- ★ some fresh cream or creamy milk
- ★ a clean piece of muslin or a soft tea towel
- ★ a strainer

1. Make sure the jar is clean.
2. Pour the milk or cream into the jar. Put the lid on very tight.
3. Shake the jar back and forth. Keep shaking until the milk looks pale and thin, and you can see little lumps of butter.

4. Put the muslin into a strainer.
5. Pour all the butter and liquid into the muslin. Leave it to drain for about 20 minutes.

You can mix a little salt with your butter. You can press it into a neat shape with a spatula. Spread it on some bread with your favourite jam.

Your butter is now ready to eat!

Do you like warm buttered toast? Mmmm!

GLOSSARY

Cells A small part of something.

Dhal A kind of curry made from lentils.

Easter The special day when Christians remember that Jesus returned from the dead.

Harvesting Picking the crops.

Neutralise To stop the effect of something and make it how it was before.

Poison Something that kills you or makes you ill.

Pollen The yellow powder inside a flower that helps to make seeds.

Ripe Describes a plant that is ready to be eaten.

Rust When a metal rusts, it is covered in an orange substance.

Star One of the bright points of the light you see in the sky at night.

Wax A substance that melts very easily and is used for making candles.

INDEX

Numbers in **bold** refer to illustrations.